The Great Connecticut Puzzle Book

By Jane Petrlik Smolik

MidRun Press
Wenham, Massachusetts
www.midrunpress.com

For
"The Cousins"

Table of Contents

This Puzzle Book is the property of.....

Name: _____

Address: _____

_____

_____

What brings me to Connecticut is.....

❏ I live here.

❏ I'm visiting relatives here.

❏ I'm vacationing here.

❏ I'm just passing through.

❏ Other.

What I like best about Connecticut is ....

_____

_____

_____

Lighthouse Logic

Bordered on its south by Long Island Sound, Connecticut has many lighthouses to warn ships away from land. Each lighthouse below has a number. Can you figure out which of the numbers 7, 9, 12, 15, and 25 go with which lighthouse?

Lighthouses 7 and 9 have windows.

Lighthouses 7 and 25 have houses attached.

Lighthouse 15 has stripes.

Place the correct number under each lighthouse.

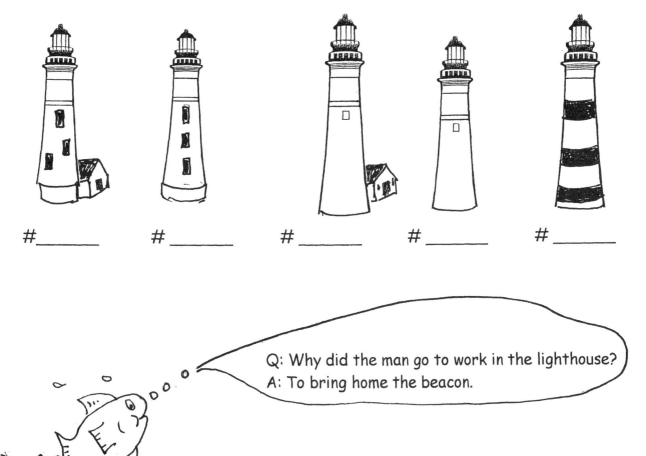

#_____   #_____   #_____   #_____   #_____

Q: Why did the man go to work in the lighthouse?
A: To bring home the beacon.

Connecticut Counties Word Search

There are eight counties in Connecticut. Find and circle them in the Word Search.

Fairfield
Hartford
Litchfield
Middlesex
New Haven
New London
Tolland
Windham

M	Z	T	D	H	N	N	P	R	E	Y	G	R	U	H
I	U	T	O	L	I	H	Y	O	M	Z	Y	A	R	A
D	K	H	K	L	E	M	R	M	Y	G	K	E	O	R
D	M	Q	B	F	L	I	J	J	Z	T	P	H	F	T
L	T	R	S	Z	K	A	F	K	H	Z	Z	A	V	F
E	M	Z	E	H	R	J	N	H	E	B	I	F	R	O
S	N	N	Q	U	G	R	E	D	C	R	H	Q	Z	R
E	O	N	F	G	B	U	A	Y	F	T	M	B	M	D
X	D	E	S	A	A	L	V	I	M	T	I	L	X	U
U	N	V	D	Y	R	B	E	A	Y	M	U	L	V	Z
U	O	A	W	G	U	L	H	H	W	Q	M	F	E	P
X	L	H	E	X	D	D	X	V	O	A	J	L	P	E
E	W	W	U	W	N	C	H	J	P	F	N	B	E	B
G	E	E	F	I	Y	V	B	Y	H	H	C	U	C	F
Y	N	N	W	S	P	V	N	J	Y	H	L	V	V	R

8

Connecticut or Bust!

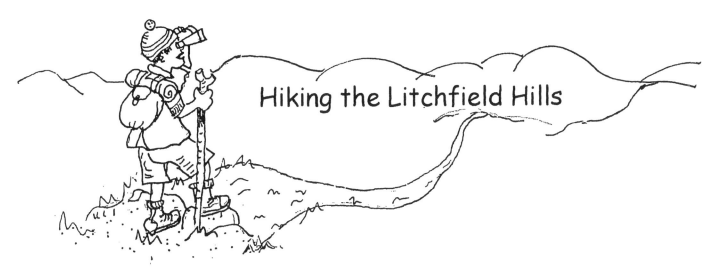

Hiking the Litchfield Hills

The Donovan family wants to go hiking in the beautiful, rolling Litchfield Hills in the northwestern corner of Connecticut. Help them find their way.

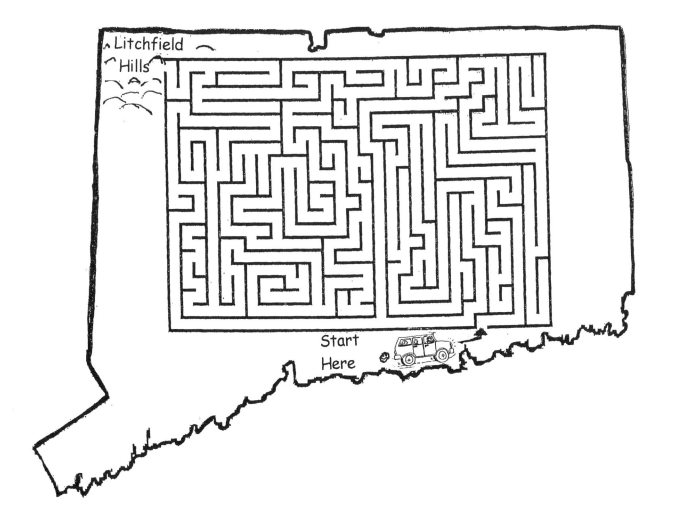

Litchfield Hills

Start Here

Noah Webster, Wordsmith (1758-1843)

Noah Webster was born in West Hartford and went to Yale, the only college in Connecticut at that time. In order to earn money to study law he taught school. But he was unhappy with the schools of that time. He felt that American children should have American textbooks, not books imported from England. So he took it upon himself to write *A Grammatical Institute of the English Language* which became a huge success.

In later years his love of words and language inspired him to compile the first American dictionary. It included 12,000 words and 40,000 definitions that had never appeared before in a dictionary. Can you imagine starting a dictionary from scratch? You can still buy newer editions of Webster's Dictionary today.

In honor of this remarkable wordsmith (someone who is a word expert), see if you can complete this puzzle.

Across

1. Largest ocean mammals
4. Word expert
6. Book of definitions
7. Webster's college
9. A building for plays and movies
10. Very good looking
11. Extremely well known

Down

2. An official rule
3. Past events
5. Books used by schools
6. Last month of the year
8. Our native language

Sea Glass

Along our beaches people love to collect small pieces of sparkling, jewel-like sea glass. These bits of beach glass start out as shards of glass or pottery from ship wrecks, pirates and even littering. They become smooth after being rolled about by the abrasive sand. They are so beautiful that jewelers make bracelets and necklaces from them and people collect them as souvenirs. The ruby red pieces are the rarest!

It is not just bottles that become precious sea glass though. Fill in the Kriss Kross with 16 items that can end up as sparkling sea glass treasure.

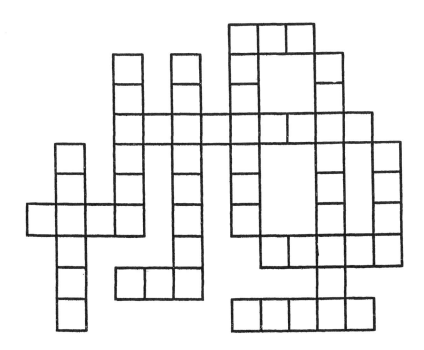

3 Letters	5 Letters	7 Letters	9 Letters
JAR	CHINA	JEWELRY	PORCELAIN
TOY	PLATE		STONEWARE

4 Letters	6 Letters	8 Letters	
JUGS	DISHES	CROCKERY	
PIPE	SAUCER		

What's Our Largest City?

The largest city in Connecticut is home to The Barnum Museum and the annual Barnum Festival. Come here to visit the "please touch" Discovery Museum and Planetarium. One of the most popular attractions here is The Beardsley Zoo. Unscramble the name of each animal that you might find at the zoo and write it in the boxes following the letters. When you are finished, read down the boxed letters to find the name of Connecticut's largest city.

ABRE   ☐ __ __ __   (hint: Some of us hibernate.)

ORONAC   ☐ __ __ __ __ __   (I have a mask.)

NLOI   __ ☐ __ __   (I roar!)

OODNRC   __ __ __ ☐ __ __   (I'm a big bird.)

IARALGLOT   __ __ __ __ ☐ __ __ __ __   (swamp dweller)

XFEOS   __ __ __ ☐ __   (Hounds chase us.)

SGPI   ☐ __ __ __   (Oink!)

SNBIO   __ __ __ ☐ __   (I roam the plains.)

ESTRTO   __ __ __ __ ☐ __   (We can swim.)

GRITE   ☐ __ __ __ __   (I'm a big cat.)

The Beardsley Zoo Word Search

The Beardsley Zoo in Bridgeport is a wonderful place to visit and see more than 300 animals, many of them endangered and threatened species.

The animals listed below can all be found at the zoo. Find and circle each one in the word search puzzle. The words appear horizontally, vertically and diagonally.

ALLIGATOR
BALD EAGLES
BEAR
BISON
CAIMANS
CONDOR
FOXES
GOATS
LION
LLAMAS
LYNX
MONKEY
OCELOT
OTTERS
PEACOCK
PIGS
PORCUPINES
PRAIRIE DOG
PRONGHORN
TIGER
TURKEYS
VULTURE
WOLVES

K	U	S	S	W	O	L	V	E	S	X	A	I	S	C	S
K	V	L	Y	N	T	I	G	E	R	G	A	O	L	A	G
T	G	S	Y	E	A	S	P	I	G	S	S	U	M	D	S
Z	R	K	R	E	K	M	E	N	U	Z	I	A	U	E	Z
F	E	T	L	E	K	R	I	L	N	A	L	F	N	G	H
G	N	N	Y	O	T	N	U	A	G	L	C	I	Y	Z	C
O	R	Y	N	J	D	T	O	T	C	A	P	X	L	Y	G
D	O	S	X	Z	U	S	O	M	R	U	E	Y	R	T	N
E	H	S	Q	E	T	L	Q	O	C	R	T	D	N	P	O
I	G	T	I	X	P	I	T	R	K	E	O	H	L	E	I
R	N	A	V	J	T	A	O	C	R	N	C	D	S	A	L
I	O	O	F	O	G	P	O	U	W	D	K	I	N	O	B
A	R	G	L	I	D	C	T	C	L	A	Y	N	B	O	S
R	P	E	L	B	A	L	B	E	A	R	Q	Y	S	E	C
P	C	L	G	E	U	F	O	X	E	S	M	S	F	I	D
O	A	K	P	V	B	I	S	O	N	G	B	X	V	H	S

MISSING LETTERS

Find the one letter in the left-hand column that is not in the word in the right-hand column. Write the extra letter in the blank space. Then read down the middle column to find one of the most exciting places to visit in Connecticut.

14

MINTY _____ TINY
PAYS _____ SAP
STUN _____ NUT
STREET _____ TREES
CASHIER _____ SEARCH
CRUEL _____ RULE

BOAST _____ BOAT
NOOSE _____ SOON
STARING _____ STRING
SLEEP _____ EELS
HOME _____ HEM
STRIDE _____ DIETS
FLOAT _____ LOAF

MUSE _____ SUE
SUNDAY _____ SANDY
SLATE _____ TEAL
STEAM _____ MAST
FAULT _____ FLAT
SCREAM _____ ACRES

GOOD NEIGHBORS!

Connecticut shares borders with 3 other states. Read the directions below and then label that state or body of water on the map.

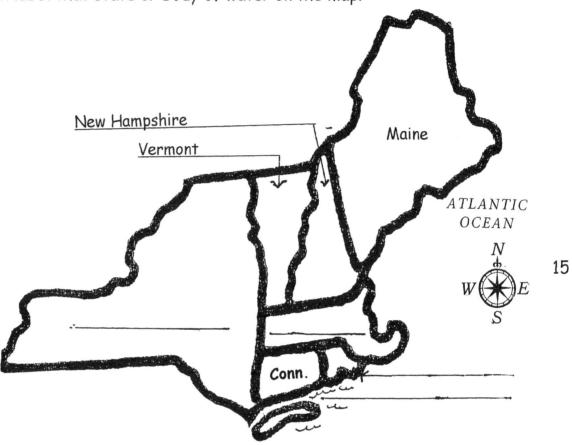

1. <u>New York</u> shares Connecticut's western border and also shares a border with Vermont. Label New York.

2. <u>Massachusetts</u> lies north of Connecticut. Label Massachusetts.

3. <u>Rhode Island</u> lies east of Connecticut and is the smallest state to share a border with us. Label Rhode Island.

4. <u>Long Island Sound</u> is a body of water located off the southern coast of Connecticut. Label Long Island Sound.

SECRET MESSAGES

1. What is the longest river within the state? Cross out all the letters B, D and A to discover the answer.

BDTHBEAADCDODNBADNECBBTIDADCDUDDBATBRDAIBVER

Write the answer here _____

2. He is considered the "father of Connecticut". Cross out all the letters U, L and P to discover the answer.

ULRLLEV.PLUTUHPUOLLMPPLASLUHOPPLUOUKPEUURPULLP

Write the answer here _____

3. What is the official state bird of Connecticut? Cross out all the letters F, S and K to discover the answer.

FTSHSESAFKSKFKKFKMSFSKSFEFRKICKFKSAFNRFOFFKBSIN

Write the answer here _____

4. Which city claims to be the home of the first pizza? Cross out all the letters R, M and B to discover the answer.

BRNBBEMWRMBHRRMBBBRRRABRVMMMERBBRMNMRBB

Write the answer here _____

I'll take mine with extra cheese!

16

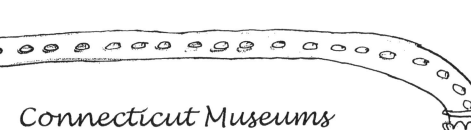

Connecticut Museums

There are many exciting museums in Connecticut. Find the location of each museum listed below by using the Code Box.

Code Box

S	J	V	D	X	I	Y	P	E	W	K	B	H
1	2	3	4	5	6	7	8	9	10	11	12	13
R	A	Q	N	G	T	L	C	M	U	Z	F	O
14	15	16	17	18	19	20	21	22	23	24	25	26

1. The location of The Connecticut River Museum (www.ctrivermuseum.org)

   $\overline{9}$ $\overline{1}$ $\overline{1}$ $\overline{9}$ $\overline{5}$

2. The location of The Discovery Museum and Planetarium (www.discoverymuseum.org)

   $\overline{12}$ $\overline{14}$ $\overline{6}$ $\overline{4}$ $\overline{18}$ $\overline{9}$ $\overline{8}$ $\overline{26}$ $\overline{14}$ $\overline{19}$

3. The location of The Lutz Children's Museum   (www.lutzmuseum.org)

   $\overline{22}$ $\overline{15}$ $\overline{17}$ $\overline{21}$ $\overline{13}$ $\overline{9}$ $\overline{1}$ $\overline{19}$ $\overline{9}$ $\overline{14}$

4. The location of the New England Carousel Museum (www.thecarouselmuseum.org)

   $\overline{12}$ $\overline{14}$ $\overline{6}$ $\overline{1}$ $\overline{19}$ $\overline{26}$ $\overline{20}$

How Many Miles?

One summer the Cardus family decided to visit some of the exciting, historic places in Connecticut. Read each leg of the trip and then find the corresponding locations on the map on the opposite page. Write down the number of miles the family drove to get from one spot to the next. Finally add up the miles and find out how far the family traveled that summer.

1. The Cardus family first drove from their home in **New Canaan** to the Maritime Aquarium in **Norwalk** where they observed sharks, jellies, and sea turtles. They drove _____ miles.

2. From **Norwalk** they traveled to **Bristol** to have some fun at Lake Compounce, the nation's oldest amusement park. They screamed their brains out on the Twister Sisters Slide. They drove _____ miles.

3. They left **Bristol** early one morning and drove _____ miles to The Lutz Children's Museum in **Manchester** where they learned some words in sign language and visited some of the injured wildlife that had been rescued.

4. From **Manchester** they drove to the beautiful town of **Mystic** and unpacked their bags. At the Mystic Aquarium they got up close to beluga whales and watched seals play. They had driven _____ miles.

5. They traveled from **Mystic** to **Middletown** so they could visit Kidcity Children's Museum. They directed their own family movie at the Video Theater. They drove _____ miles from Mystic to Middletown.

6. Finally, the weary Cardus family drove from **Middletown** back to their home sweet home in **New Canaan.** They drove _____ miles.

Question: How many miles in all did the Cardus family travel that summer?

Answer: _____ miles

How Many Miles?

Use this map to answer the questions on the opposite page.

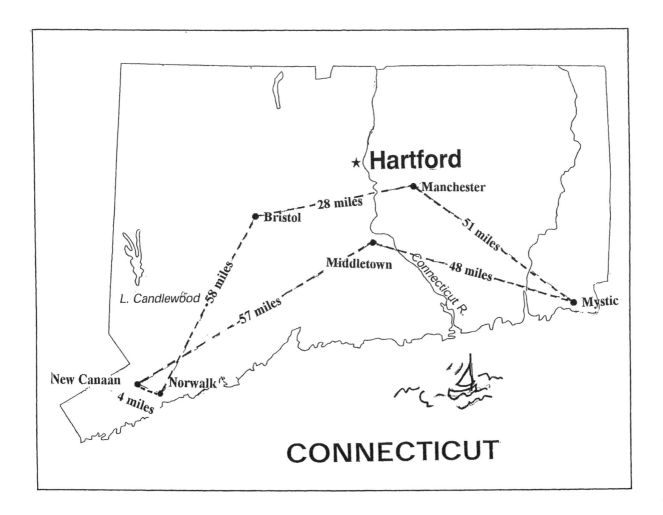

★ **Hartford**

Manchester

Bristol — 28 miles

51 miles

L. Candlewood

58 miles

Middletown

Connecticut R.

48 miles

Mystic

57 miles

New Canaan •Norwalk

4 miles

CONNECTICUT

Question: What did Delaware?
Answer: Her New Jersey.

Question: Why did the watch go on vacation?
Answer: It wanted to unwind.

Lake Candlewood Word Search

There are hundreds of lakes in Connecticut and some of the larger ones are used as reservoirs. The largest lake, Lake Candlewood, was manmade to store water for generating electricity. It is the third largest constructed lake in the world! It extends through the towns of Danbury, Brookfield and New Fairfield. While several kinds of fish can be found in the lake's waters, many animals roam in the surrounding woods and fields. Find and circle animals listed below that might be found in this area.

L	E	T	M	W	M	U	S	S	O	P	P	O
P	E	N	A	E	X	Y	K	R	E	T	T	O
X	M	M	I	C	B	A	T	I	P	A	M	K
J	I	F	M	P	B	V	G	Z	S	F	C	D
S	N	O	E	I	U	O	E	L	H	U	F	U
T	K	X	C	D	N	C	B	R	H	Q	O	C
I	S	K	J	A	F	G	R	C	M	O	I	S
B	S	H	Y	I	E	R	D	O	U	I	N	I
B	Z	V	S	T	E	O	Q	M	P	Q	N	L
A	B	H	O	V	O	T	B	H	O	R	P	E
R	E	Y	A	W	Z	K	J	P	J	O	Y	Y
R	O	E	B	E	A	R	T	W	Y	H	S	M
C	B	M	U	S	K	R	A	T	G	X	Z	E

BAT
BEAR
BEAVER
BOBCAT
COYOTE
ERMINE
FISHER
FOX
LEMMING
MINK
MOOSE
MUSKRAT
OPPOSSUM
OTTER
PORCUPINE
RABBITS
WOODCHUCK

Q: What do ducks eat?
A: Quackers.

Mitten Match

After skiing, sledding and skating, a pile of unmatched mittens need to be sorted. There is one mitten without a match. (This comes as no surprise to mothers.) Circle the mitten below that does not have a partner.

21

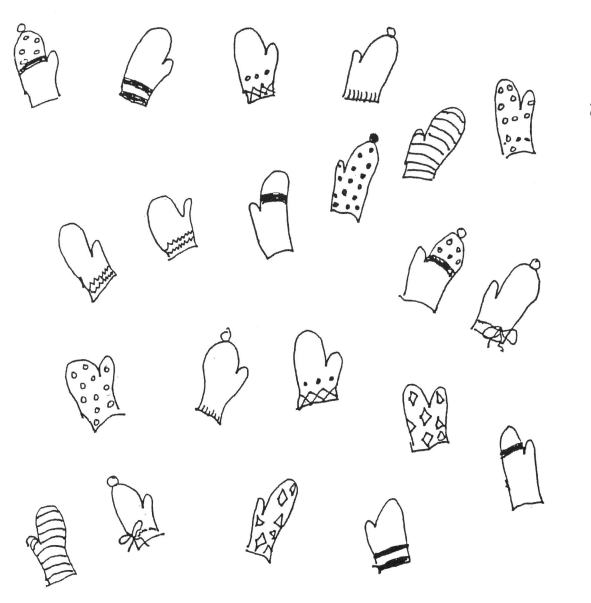

More Connecticut Museums

There are so many exciting museums in Connecticut we had to make another page to name some more! Find the location of each museum listed below by using the Code Box.

Code Box

S	J	V	D	X	I	Y	P	E	W	K	B	H
1	2	3	4	5	6	7	8	9	10	11	12	13
R	A	Q	N	G	T	L	C	M	U	Z	F	O
14	15	16	17	18	19	20	21	22	23	24	25	26

1. The location of The Connecticut Trolley Museum (www.ceraonline.org)

   $\overline{}\ \overline{}\ \overline{}\ \overline{}\quad\overline{}\ \overline{}\ \overline{}\ \overline{}\ \overline{}\ \overline{}\ \overline{}$
     9   15 1   19   10 6   17   4   1   26 14

2. The location of the Mystic Seaport and Museum (www.mysticseaport.org)

   $\overline{}\ \overline{}\ \overline{}\ \overline{}\ \overline{}\ \overline{}$
    22   7   1   19 6   21

3. The location of the Stepping Stones Museum for Children (www.steppingstonesmuseum.org)

   $\overline{}\ \overline{}\ \overline{}\ \overline{}\ \overline{}\ \overline{}\ \overline{}$
    17 26 14 10 15 20   11

4. The location of Kidcity Children's Museum (www.kidcitymuseum.com)

   $\overline{}\ \overline{}\ \overline{}\ \overline{}\ \overline{}\ \overline{}\ \overline{}\ \overline{}\ \overline{}\ \overline{}$
    22   6   4   4   20 9   19 26 10 17

Word Pyramids

'CT' is the United States Post Office's abbreviation for Connecticut. We have written 'CT' in the first row of each word pyramid. Write a three-letter word that contains those two letters in the next row. (The letters can appear in any order in the word.) Now use those three letters to make a four-letter word in the next line. Keep going until you finish each pyramid. We've done one to show you how it's done.

Example

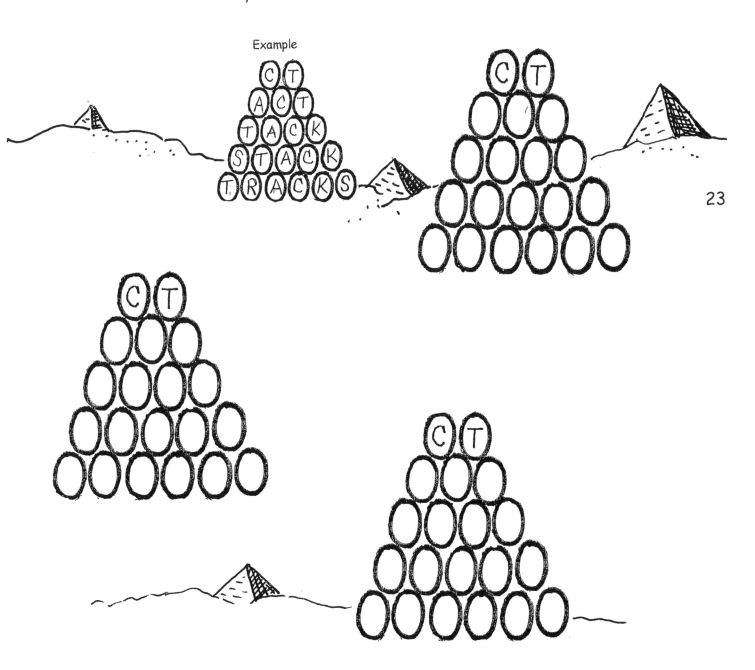

23

"The Nutmeg State" Cross Outs

Our nickname, "The Nutmeg State", comes from colonial days when traveling salesmen went from town to town with their horse and wagon. From inside their covered wagons they sold tools, books, pots and pans, and spices to the colonists.

Nutmeg was a popular spice but very difficult to get as the round, brown nut grows only on trees in distant tropical countries. They quickly sold out of the few nuts they had. Rather than miss a sale, some dishonest peddlers would carve fake nutmegs out of wood and sell them as the real thing, which is how we got our nickname.

Follow the instructions to find two interesting facts about nutmegs.

1. Cross out 4 animals.
2. Cross out 3 foreign countries.
3. Cross out 2 New England cities.
4. Cross out 3 types of weather.

DOG	THE	FRANCE	BOSTON	SPICE
RAIN	CAT	COMES	RUSSIA	SNOW
FROM	HARTFORD	GOAT	THE	CHINA
TREE'S	ZEBRA	BROWN	HURRICANE	SEEDS

1. Cross out 3 school subjects.
2. Cross out 3 colors.
3. Cross out 3 states.

MATH	NUTMEG	HISTORY	YELLOW	IS
A	PURPLE	SWEET	OHIO	TEXAS
SPICY	SCIENCE	GREEN	FLAVOR	FLORIDA

Nutmeg Recipe

Nutmeg is much easier to buy today than it was back in colonial days.
And you can be sure when you buy it in your grocery store that it's not a fake!

Yummy Apple Crisp

1 cup graham cracker crumbs
1 tablespoon flour
1 cup chopped pecans
1 cup brown sugar
1/4 cup granulated sugar
4 tablespoons butter, melted
1 tablespoon freshly grated orange rind
Dash of salt
½ teaspoon cinnamon
½ teaspoon ground nutmeg
4 large tart apples

Preheat oven to 400°
Mix the first five ingredients. Add the orange rind, salt, cinnamon and nutmeg.
Add the melted butter. Lightly butter a small baking dish. Peel, core and thinly
slice apples and place slices on the bottom of the dish. Scatter crumb mixture
over the top and bake for 45 minutes until golden brown. Serves 6.

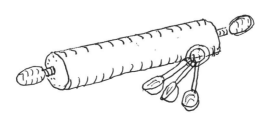

Nutmeg in a Maze

Emily wants to make the Yummy Apple Crisp recipe on the previous page but she's misplaced her nutmeg. Help her find her way to this tasty nut.

Still More Connecticut Museums

There are so many exciting museums in Connecticut we had to make another page to name some more! Find the location of each museum listed below by using the Code Box.

Code Box

S	J	V	D	X	I	Y	P	E	W	K	B	H
1	2	3	4	5	6	7	8	9	10	11	12	13
R	A	Q	N	G	T	L	C	M	U	Z	F	O
14	15	16	17	18	19	20	21	22	23	24	25	26

1. The location of The Children's Museum of Southeastern Connecticut (www.childrensmuseumsect.org)

   __ __ __ __ __ __ __
   17 6 15 17 19 6 21

2. The location of The Connecticut Children's Museum (www.childrensbuilding.org)

   __ __ __   __ __ __ __ __
   17 9 10   13 15 3 9 17

3. The location of Imagine Nation Children's Museum (www.familycenter.org/ImagineNation)

   __ __ __ __ __ __ __
   12 14 6 1 19 26 20

4. The location of The Science Center of Connecticut (www.sciencecenterct.org)

   __ __ __ __   __ __ __ __ __ __ __ __
   10 9 1 19   13 15 14 19 25 26 14 4

Connecticut Favorites

The four children in the Yermal family each have a different favorite bird or animal in Connecticut. Use the information given below to find out which each child likes best. Mark an X in a square when it *cannot* be the answer. Mark an O to show the favorite.

1. Clams are not Bill's favorite.
2. Sue does not like oysters.
3. Sarah likes robins better than lobsters.
4. Bob's favorite are clams.
5. Sarah likes oysters better than robins.
6. Bill prefers lobsters to robins.

28

CHILD	Oysters	Robins	Clams	Lobsters
Bill				
Sarah				
Bob				
Sue				

VISIT CONNECTICUT IN THE SUMMER

You are in charge of trying to get tourists to come and visit Connecticut. In the frame below make your own poster or brochure that would encourage people to come to the Nutmeg State in the SUMMER.

29

VISIT CONNECTICUT IN THE WINTER

You are in charge of trying to get tourists to come and visit Connecticut. In the frame below make your own poster or brochure that would encourage people to come to the Nutmeg State in the WINTER.

30

Connecticut Legends

A legend is a story that is repeated over and over again often changing along the way. It is sometimes made up of some facts and some myths. Or it may be entirely untrue. Connecticut has a long history of legends and folklore. Read about these four legends and see for yourself!

The Old Leatherman

Since 1862, the true story has been told of a man who wandered for 30 years in a 365-mile circle between the Connecticut and Hudson Rivers. He was given the nickname, Old Leatherman, because he was always dressed from head to toe in scraps of leather that were poorly stitched together. They even squeaked when he walked. But they helped to protect him from the harsh New England winters as he only slept outside, usually in caves.

He never spoke but communicated with grunts and hand gestures.

His real name was Jules Bourglay and he was born and grew up in Lyons, France. After a broken love affair, he came to America by boat where he began his constant wanderings. He would arrive in each town on exactly the same day each year. People in Haddam, Connecticut even claimed you could set your watch by his arrival.

He died one cold winter in 1889 in a cave in Ossining, New York.

To this day western Connecticut is marked with "Leatherman's Caves" including one that is located on the Mattatuck Trail in Watertown, Connecticut.

The Charter Oak

This is perhaps the best known legend in Connecticut history. In April 1662, King Charles II granted Connecticut a Charter saying that they could run most of their own affairs. But five years later, a new King James II decided to bring Connecticut back under English control. He demanded that Connecticut's leaders give up the Charter. They refused.

So the new king sent Edmund Andros over to govern all of New England. In a meeting in what is now Hartford, Andros demanded he be given the piece of paper that contained the Charter. It was nighttime and suddenly the candles went out in the meeting room. In the darkness, the Charter was handed out an open window to a Captain Wadsworth who hid it in the hollow of a big, 800-year old oak tree until Andros had departed.

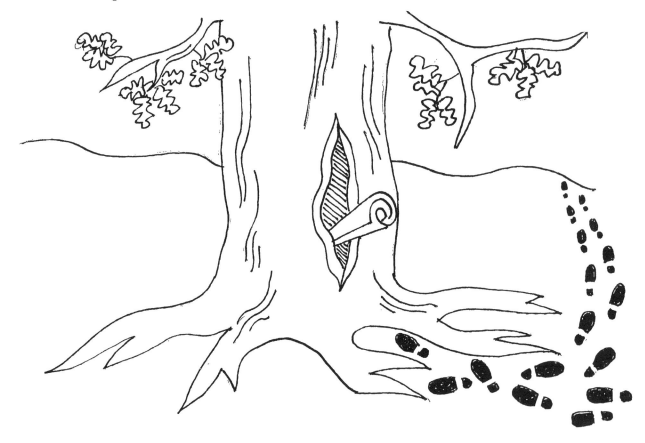

When the tree was blown down during a storm in 1856, the entire state was saddened over the loss of the beloved tree.

A plaque now marks the spot in Hartford where the great oak stood.

The Black Dog of West Peak

The Black Dog has been described as having sad eyes, a bark that makes no sound, and feet that leave no footprints behind. Supposedly, he roams West Peak in the Hanging Hills of Meriden, Connecticut.

The first time people see him they enjoy his quiet company. But legend has it that if a person sees him three times, tragedy will befall them!

People claim that he is a friendly little dog, that looks a little like a spaniel. The following verse is often repeated:

"*If a man shall meet the Black Dog once, it shall be for joy; and if twice, it shall be for sorrow; and the third time, he shall die.*"

So when someone meets a sudden, accidental death people around Meriden say, "The poor soul must have seen the Black Dog once too often."

To this day, hikers claim to see this friendly dog, wagging his tail, leaving no footprints and barking with no sound.

Pirate Gold

Around 1698 the pirate Captain Kidd began looting ships as they entered New York harbor, loaded with valuables. It is known that he buried twenty- four treasure chests on Gardiner's Island, off the coast of eastern Long Island. John Gardiner, the lord of the island, even gave Kidd an itemized receipt dated July 17, 1699 listing the gold, silver and jewels hidden there.

But the pirate was captured in 1699 before he could return for his loot and he was hanged in London in 1701. The governor of the Massachusetts Bay Colony then demanded that Lord John Gardiner return the treasure to them, which he did.

In spite of the records of the Massachusetts Bay Colony, people still look for other stashes of pirate treasure along the Connecticut coastline. It is known that Captain Kidd and other lesser known pirates, sailed the coves and islands of Long Island Sound and even visited the town of Milford, Connecticut.

THE LEATHERMAN MAZE

The Leatherman is roaming through the hills and it's starting to get dark. Help him find his way back to his cave.

Pirate's Maze

Captain Kidd can't remember where he hid his chest of gold and silver. Help him find his way to the buried treasure.

36

Connecticut Legends Crossword Puzzle

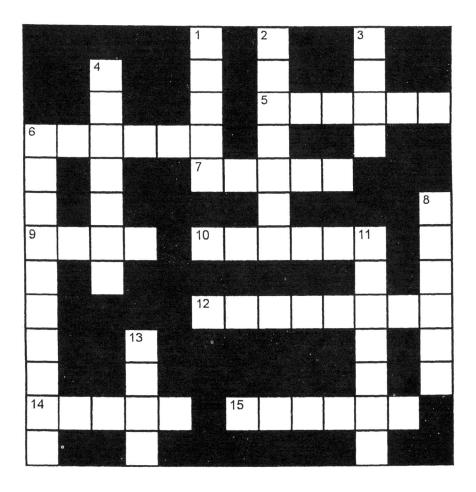

Read about the four Connecticut legends on page 31 and then do the crossword below.

37

Across

5. The city where the pirate was hung
6. Foreign country where The Leatherman was born
7. The Charter Oak fell down during a ___
9. What the Charter Oak is
10. Town that set their watches by Leatherman
12. Captain Kidd was _____ in 1699
14. Number of times you *don't* want to see the Black Dog
15. Pirates buried gold, _____ and jewels

Down

1. Leatherman usually slept in these
2. Connecticut town pirate Captain visited
3. The pirate, Captain _____
4. Material that gave Jules Bourglay his nickname
6. The Black Dog left no _____
8. The Charter was passed out an open _____
11. Town where Black Dog is seen
13. The Black Dog has sad _____

C T

The U.S. Post Office's two-letter abbreviation for the state of Connecticut is CT - the first and last letters of its name. The answer to each definition below is a word containing the letters CT.

1. A feline pet   C _ T

2. The least valuable coin   C _ _ T

3. Land next to the sea   C _ _ _ T

4. Orange root vegetable   C _ _ _ _ T

5. Agree   C _ _ _ _ _ T

6. Type of tree or reddish-brown horse   C _ _ _ _ _ _ T

KEEP UP THE GOOD WORK!

TO:
The Governor
State House
Hartford, CT
06101

Long Island Sound

Long Island Sound is an *estuary*, a place where seawater mixes with freshwater. Estuaries are among the most productive ecosystems on Earth. Approximately 8 million people live near the Sound and millions more vacation here every year. Use the Code Box to learn some interesting facts about the area.

Code Box

S	J	V	D	X	I	Y	P	E	W	K	B	H
1	2	3	4	5	6	7	8	9	10	11	12	13
R	A	Q	N	G	T	L	C	M	U	Z	F	O
14	15	16	17	18	19	20	21	22	23	24	25	26

1. The freshwater that mixes with seawater in the Sound comes mostly from these three

sources; __ __ __   __ __ __ __ __ __ __ __ __ __ ,
     19 13 9   21 26 17 17 9 21 19 6 21 23 19

__ __ __ __ __ __ __ __ __ __ ,   __ __ __
13 26 23 1 15 19 26 17 6 21   15 17 4

__ __ __ __ __ __   __ __ __ __ __ __ .
19 13 15 22 9 1   14 6 3 9 14 1

2. To get close to the marine life of Long Island Sound you should visit The Maritime

Center at __ __ __ __ __ __ __   and The Marinelife Aquarium in
       17 26 14 10 15 20 11

__ __ __ __ __ .
9 1 1 9 5

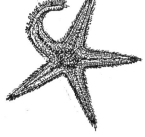

Mapping Connecticut

A **distance scale** shows you the number of miles between places so you can measure the distance. Using the distance scale and map on the opposite page, write down the approximate number of miles it is from each place to the other.

map

This is an example of a distance scale.

1   10   20   30   40   50 miles

1. Hartford to Putnam _____ miles

2. Putnam to Mystic _____ miles

3. Danbury to Bridgeport _____ miles

4. Canaan to New Haven _____ miles

5. Bridgeport to Stafford Springs _____ miles

6. Norwalk to Waterbury _____ miles

7. New London to Mystic _____ miles

8. Canaan to Stafford Springs _____ miles

9. Stamford to Shelton _____ miles

Now you've got it. Good for you. All maps have **distance scales** so you just learned a map skill that you will be able to use for the rest of your life.

Mapping Connecticut

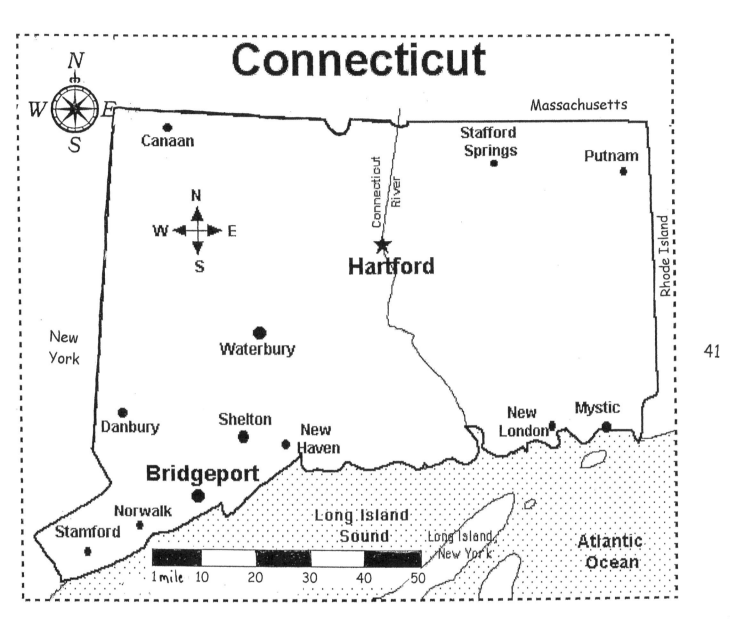

Connecticut

Massachusetts

Canaan

Stafford Springs

Putnam

Connecticut River

Rhode Island

Hartford

New York

Waterbury

41

Danbury

Shelton

New Haven

New London

Mystic

Bridgeport

Norwalk

Stamford

Long Island Sound

Long Island, New York

Atlantic Ocean

1 mile 10 20 30 40 50

The compass rose is an icon that map makers place on a map to show which direction is north, south, east and west.

Beaches Criss Cross

People flock to the many beautiful beaches that edge Long Island Sound. Fit the names of the beaches listed below into the puzzle squares.

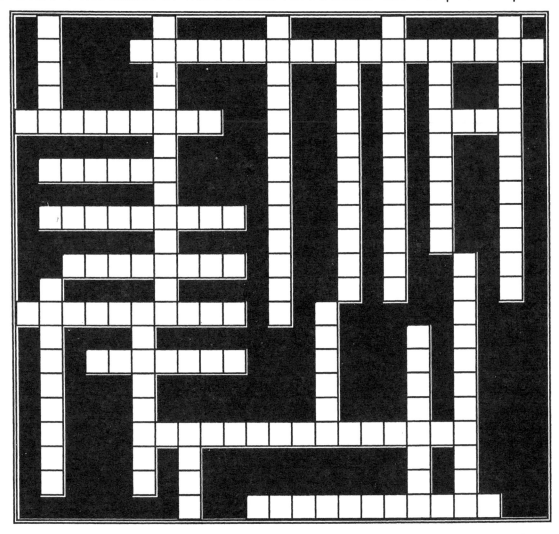

4 Letters	8 Letters	11 Letters	13 Letters
GULF	JENNINGS	CALF PASTURE	HOLE-IN-THE-WALL
TOWN	RICKARDS	HAMMONASSET	PEAR TREE POINT
	SURF CLUB	SEASIDE PARK	
5 Letters			15 Letters
SASCO	9 Letters	12 Letters	LIGHTHOUSE
	EAST WHARF	EASTERN POINT	POINT
6 Letters	SOUND VIEW	GREENS HARBOR	
JACOBS	SOUTHPORT		18 Letters
WALNUT	WEED BEACH		ROCKY NECK STATE
			PARK
7 Letters	10 Letters		
HARVEYS	COVE ISLAND		

← Don't forget your sunscreen!

Counting Seashells

After a morning spent collecting shells at the seashore the children sit down to see how many shells each child collected. Read all the clues. Then write the correct child's name next to the number of shells he or she found.

NAME	NUMBER OF SHELLS
A. _____	20
B. _____	12
C. _____	8
D. _____	7
E. _____	5

1. Will has 3 green shells and 2 white shells.
2. Katie has 3 more shells than Will.
3. Tim has the most shells.
4. John and Katie together have the same number of shells as Tim.
5. How big is Melanie's collection? _____

Question: What kind of hair does the ocean have?
Answer: Wavy.

Question: What kind of waves are impossible to swim in?
Answer: Microwaves.

TIDE POOLING CRISS CROSS

Tide pools are pockets of ocean water left in the rocks when the tide goes out. It is a world in miniature where plants and animals live together. Many small creatures are trapped in the tide pools until the tide comes back in and they can swim away. Tide pools are filled with hundreds of different kinds of tiny plants and animals that are called *plankton.*

Fit the words that relate to tide pools into the puzzle squares.

4 Letters	7 Letters	9 Letters
KELP	ANIMALS	BARNACLES
SAND	MUSSELS	CREATURES
TIDE	OYSTERS	
	SEAWEED	11 Letters
5 Letters	URCHINS	PERIWINKLES
CLAMS		
~~CRABS~~	8 Letters	
OCEAN	ANEMONES	
ROCKS	FLOATING	
	PLANKTON	
6 Letters	STARFISH	
PLANTS		
SHELLS		

Five Senses in Connecticut

There are many things to see, hear, taste and smell in the great state of Connecticut. Put a check mark in the box next to each thing you have experienced.

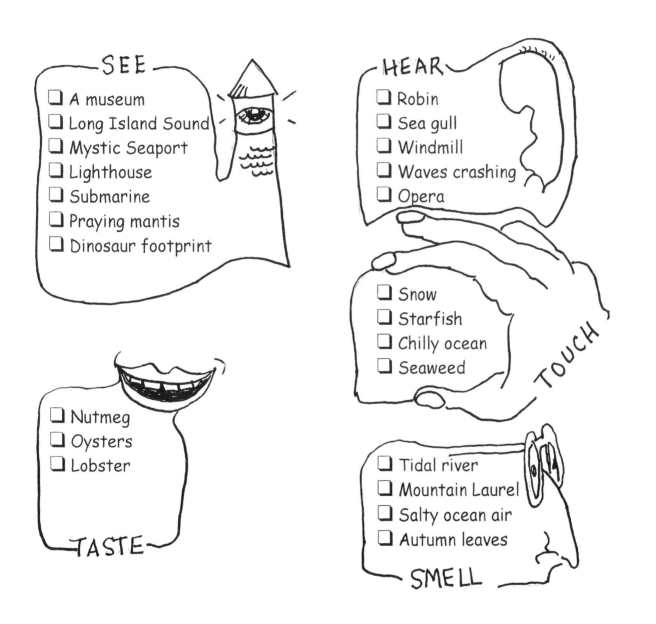

SEE
- ❏ A museum
- ❏ Long Island Sound
- ❏ Mystic Seaport
- ❏ Lighthouse
- ❏ Submarine
- ❏ Praying mantis
- ❏ Dinosaur footprint

HEAR
- ❏ Robin
- ❏ Sea gull
- ❏ Windmill
- ❏ Waves crashing
- ❏ Opera

TOUCH
- ❏ Snow
- ❏ Starfish
- ❏ Chilly ocean
- ❏ Seaweed

TASTE
- ❏ Nutmeg
- ❏ Oysters
- ❏ Lobster

SMELL
- ❏ Tidal river
- ❏ Mountain Laurel
- ❏ Salty ocean air
- ❏ Autumn leaves

45

Categories

Connecticut is the third smallest state in the United States. Only Delaware and Rhode Island are smaller. Here's one way to remember that it's the THIRD smallest state. In each box below write the name of something that fits in the category at left and begins with the letter at the top. We've given you an example to get you started.

	T	H	I	R	D
Animal or bird	TIGER				
Words containing the letter "A"					
Things found outdoors					
Things found in the kitchen					
Girl's names					
Boy's names					

Climbing Mount Frissell

Mount Frissell, rising 2,380 feet in western Connecticut, is the state's highest point. Help Taylor climb to the top. Read each clue. Write the matching word found in the maze as you trace a path from Taylor to the top of Mount Frissell.

Clues

1. Paid money for something

   _____

2. The state capital of Connecticut

   _____

3. Worn when it gets chilly

   _____

4. Needed to mail a letter

   _____

5. Find it in a garden _____

6. A car engine _____

7. Connecticut's hottest month

   _____

8. Window decoration _____

9. You read it _____

10. Four weeks or 30 days

    _____

11. Great affection _____

2,380 feet

red   love

thing   month

tree   curtain   book

July   motor   autumn

gorilla   flower   stamp

rain   bologna   sweater

Hartford   Trumbull   Sharon

bought   fought   thought

47

START HERE

Sea level at Long Island Sound is the state's lowest point.

How's the Weather?

While Connecticut is a small state it experiences a wide variety of weather. They say if you don't like the weather in New England, just wait a minute. Can you unscramble all the jumbled words below to form the names of 12 types of weather that can occur in Connecticut throughout the year? We have given you the first letter of the first word to start you off.

1. WRONSSMTO   S_____

2. IHLA _____

3. YUMIDHTI _____

4. RAZLIZBD _____

5. CRAIHUREN _____

6. THILGGNIN _____

7. OGF _____

8. NEHDRTU _____

9. SNEHUNSI _____

10. NDWI _____

11. TELSE _____

12. IRAN _____

Licence Plate Game

People from all over the United States visit Connecticut. If you don't believe it, just try driving to the beach on a Friday in the summer! See how many licence plates from other states you can spot. Then mark an "X" next to the state. There is no time limit on how long you have to complete this game.

Alabama _____
Alaska _____
Arizona _____
Arkansas _____
California _____
Colorado _____
Connecticut _____
Delaware _____
District of Columbia
_____
Florida _____
Georgia _____
Hawaii _____
Idaho _____
Illinois _____
Indiana _____
Iowa _____
Kansas _____
Kentucky _____
Louisiana _____
Maine _____

Maryland _____
Massachusetts_____
Michigan _____
Minnesota _____
Mississippi _____
Missouri _____
Montana _____
Nebraska _____
Nevada _____
New Hampshire _____
New Jersey _____
New Mexico _____
New York _____
North Carolina _____
North Dakota _____
Ohio _____
Oklahoma _____
Oregon _____
Pennsylvania _____
Rhode Island _____
South Carolina _____

South Dakota _____
Tennessee _____
Texas _____
Utah _____
Vermont _____
Virginia _____
Washington _____
West Virginia _____
Wisconsin _____
Wyoming _____

The Dot Game

This game needs two players. Take turns drawing a horizontal or vertical line between two dots. The player that draws a line that completes a square writes his or her initial inside that completed square. It helps if you each use a different colored pencil or pen. When all the squares are connected, count how many squares each player connected. Each square is worth one point each or two points if it contains an oak leaf. Whoever has the most points wins.

Did you know that oaks are a species of large trees that produce acorns and the white oak is the official tree of Connecticut?

Player #1 Score _____   Player #2 Score _____

The Amistad Case

In June 1839, the Spanish ship *Amistad* left Havana, Cuba with 53 Africans aboard. They had been kidnaped from their African homeland. The *Amistad* was to deliver the slaves to another port in Cuba. But soon after the ship left Havana the Africans seized control of the ship and forced the Spaniards to sail towards Africa.

At night, however, the ships owners would sail northward - heading towards the Southern slave states in America.

They landed instead in Long Island Sound. The Africans were placed in a New Haven jail to await trial. Should they be considered slaves or be set free to return to Africa? A long trial took place and in 1841, the U.S. Supreme Court declared they should be free.

Question: While they waited to raise enough money to return to Africa, the 38 survivors of the *Amistad* lived in what Connecticut town?

Find the one letter in the word in the left-hand column that is not in the word in the right-hand column. Write the extra letter in the blank space. Then read down the column for the answer.

FROST	_____	ROTS
BEARD	_____	BRED
FRIEND	_____	FINED
STAMMER	_____	STREAM
PIERCE	_____	CREPE
DROWN	_____	WORD
GROWTH	_____	THROW
WASTED	_____	WADES
HOIST	_____	THIS
SPRING	_____	GRIPS

To learn more about this historical event, rent the movie *Amistad*, directed by Steven Spielberg or visit Hartford's Wadsworth Atheneum. Mystic Seaport has a wonderful replica of the famous schooner that gives you a sense of how awful the conditions were on board.

Amistad Maze

The Africans used the sun as their guide to try and sail back towards Africa. Help them navigate east towards their homeland.

AFRICA

Atlantic Ocean

An Oyster Eating Contest

While oysters are harvested all along Long Island Sound, Norwalk is considered Connecticut's Oyster Capital based on the weight of the catch. A group of children held an oyster eating contest. Read all the clues. Then write the correct names next to the number of oysters he or she ate.

NAME	Number of Oysters
A. _____	16
B. _____	12
C. _____	10
D. _____	6
E. _____	4

1. Taylor ate the most oysters.

2. Gabe ate 10 less than Taylor

3. Holly did not eat more than Gabe.

4. Sam ate more than Gabe, but less than Emily.

Q: Why won't an oyster lend you money?
A: Because they are shellfish.

The Dot Game

This game needs two players. Take turns drawing a horizontal or vertical line between two dots. The player that draws a line that completes a square writes his or her initial inside that completed square. It helps if you each use a different colored pencil or pen. When all the squares are connected, count how many squares each player connected. Each square is worth one point each or two points if it contains a nutmeg. Whoever has the most points wins.

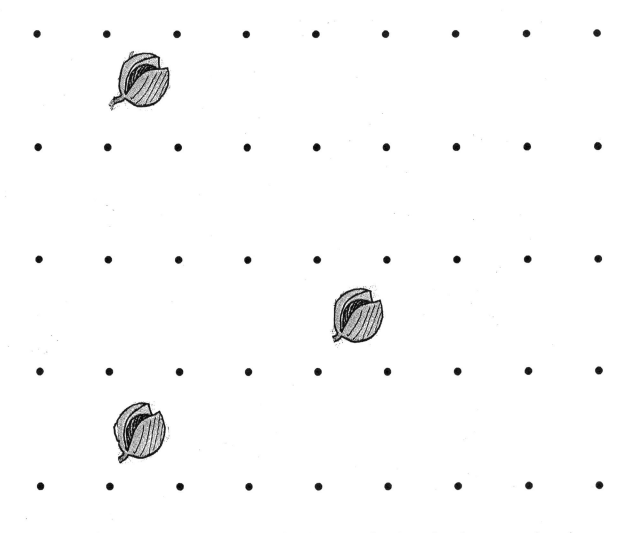

54

The nutmeg is a tropical tree that is grown for the spice that comes from its brown seeds.

Player #1 Score _____   Player #2 Score _____

Connecticut Fairs and Festivals

Throughout the year, Connecticut's towns and cities host a wide variety of interesting fairs and festivals. Below are listed just a sampling of those that you might enjoy. Using the Code Box, find out the location of each of these special events.

Code Box

S	J	V	D	X	I	Y	P	E	W	K	B	H
1	2	3	4	5	6	7	8	9	10	11	12	13

R	A	Q	N	G	T	L	C	M	U	Z	F	O
14	15	16	17	18	19	20	21	22	23	24	25	26

1. International Festival of Arts and Ideas

 ___ ___ ___   ___ ___ ___ ___ ___
 17   9   10   13   15   3   9   17

2. Hot Steamed Jazz Festival

 ___ ___ ___ ___ ___
  9   1   1   9   5

3. Sea Music Festival

 ___ ___ ___ ___ ___ ___   ___ ___ ___ ___ ___ ___ ___
 22   7   1   19   6   21   1   9   15   8   26   14   19

4. The Barnum Festival

 ___ ___ ___ ___ ___ ___ ___ ___ ___ ___
 12   14   6   4   18   9   8   26   14   19

Connecticut's Oldest Fair

Have you visited the oldest fair in the state? Using the Code Box fill in the missing words to find out about this event that is truly fun for all ages!

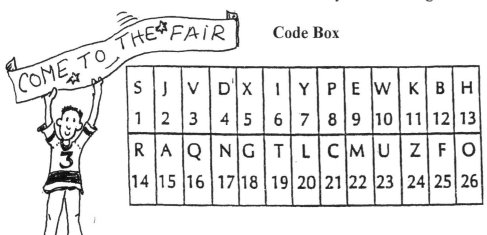

Code Box

S	J	V	D	X	I	Y	P	E	W	K	B	H
1	2	3	4	5	6	7	8	9	10	11	12	13
R	A	Q	N	G	T	L	C	M	U	Z	F	O
14	15	16	17	18	19	20	21	22	23	24	25	26

The Four Town Fair got its name because it began by traveling through each of the four towns until it found its permanent home at the __ __ __ __ __
9 18 7 8 19

__ __ __ __ fairgrounds in __ __ __ __ __ __ .
14 26 15 4   1   26 22 9 14 1

The Fair takes place in __ __ __ __ __ __ __ __ __ each year.
1   9   8   19 9 22 12 9 14

There is a __ __ __ __   __ __ __ __ __ __ __ and
25 14 26 18   2 23 22 8 6 17 18

largest __ __ __ __ contest.   Come to the Four Town Fair to see the
25 14 26 18

__ __ __ __ __ __ __ __ __ , __ __ __ __ __ __
4 26 26 4 20 9 12 23 18   14 15 21 6 17 18

__ __ __ __ and the area's largest __ __ __ __ __ __ __ .
8 6 18 1   8 23 22 8 11 6 17

Kids also love to participate in the pulls, the livestock shows, raffles, chicken barbecue, bingo, the midway as well as the many exhibits and displays.

Crossword Puzzle Tournament

The nation's oldest and largest crossword puzzle tournament takes place every year in Stamford, Connecticut. Prizes are awarded in several categories, including a $4,000 grand prize! Try your hand at the puzzle below.

Across

1. State north of Connecticut
5. Long Island _____
6. Summer beach activity
7. Remove a pencil mark
11. The Hartford Courant is the oldest
12. Often
13. Educate
14. Flowers grow here

Down

2. Connecticut before becoming a state
3. Sport played on a court with a racket and net
4. What the *Amistad* was
6. City that hosts the oldest crossword puzzle tournament
8. Ocean off Connecticut's coast
9. Connecticut's capital city
10. Snowy season

Pequot Cross-Outs

Long before the Europeans settled Connecticut, the area was inhabited by hundreds of American Indian groups. The Wappinger, Quinnipiac, Mohegan, Podunk and Niantic tribes all lived here. The most powerful of all, however, were the warlike Pequots.

They controlled the area east of the Connecticut River and eventually tensions arose with the colonists over land. In the Pequot War of 1637, the English with help from the Mohegan tribe, practically wiped out the Pequots in a terrible war that took place at Mystic.

The Mashantucket Pequot Museum in Mashantucket is the world's largest Native American museum with four *acres* of permanent exhibits. It's a popular and exciting place to visit. (www.pequotmuseum.org)

Follow the instructions to find an interesting fact about the Pequots.

1. Cross out 4 animals you might find in a zoo.
2. Cross out 3 colors.
3. Cross out 3 insects.
4. Cross out 2 boys names.

LION	THEY	TIGER	BELIEVED	YELLOW
FLY	THAT	GREEN	ZEBRA	LAND
BELONGED	ANT	JACK	TO	PINK
BEE	NO	ONE	GIRAFFE	TAYLOR

Follow the instructions to find another fact about the Peqouts.

1. Cross out 3 school subjects.
2. Cross out 2 fruits.
3. Cross out 3 pieces of clothing.

ENGLISH	THEY	APPLES	SHIRT	RAISED
CORN	HISTORY	HAT	BEANS	MATH
SQUASH	LEMONS	AND	PANTS	TOBACCO

The Dot Game

This game needs two players. Take turns drawing a horizontal or vertical line between two dots. The player that draws a line that completes a square writes his or her initial inside that completed square. It helps if you each use a different colored pencil or pen. When all the squares are connected, count how many squares each player connected. Each square is worth one point each or two points if it contains a snowflake. Whoever has the most points wins.

59

Did you know that while no two snowflakes are exactly the same all snowflakes have six sides?

Player #1 Score _____   Player #2 Score _____

Thimble Island Criss Cross

The Thimbles are a group of several small islands in Long Island Sound. They were named for the thimbleberry that grows there. Wonderful stories abound about how each one got its name. Cut-in-Two Island was home to a "beautiful midget" with whom Tom Thumb fell in love. Money Island is one of the many spots along this stretch of water where Captain Kidd supposedly buried his treasure. Fit the Thimble Islands listed below in the Criss Cross.

3 Letters	5 Letters	7 Letters	11 Letters
POT	HORSE	FRISBEE	GHOST ISLAND
	KIDDS		MOTHER-IN-LAW
4 Letters	MONEY	8 Letters	
BEAR	OUTER	CUT-IN-TWO	12 Letters
HIGH		EAST CRIB	HEN AND POTATO
	6 Letters	9 Letters	13 Letters
	BELDEN	GOVERNORS	LITTLE PUMPKIN
	ROGERS		

What River Am I?   #1

I begin in Canada and travel 410 miles to empty into Long Island Sound at Old Saybrook. Indians and early white settlers built the state's first towns along my banks. I also run through the capital city of Hartford.

Use the Code Box below to write the letters above the numbered spaces.

Code Box

S	J	V	D	X	I	Y	P	E	W	K	B	H
1	2	3	4	5	6	7	8	9	10	11	12	13
R	A	Q	N	G	T	L	C	M	U	Z	F	O
14	15	16	17	18	19	20	21	22	23	24	25	26

The following describes me.

___ ___ ___ ___ ___ ___ ___ ___ ___ ___ ___ ___ ___ ___
6   15 22 17 9   10   9   17 18 20 15 17 4   1

___ ___ ___ ___ ___ ___ ___   ___ ___ ___ ___ ___.
20 26 17 18 9   1   19   14 6   3   9   14

I am the ___ ___ ___ ___ ___ ___ ___ ___ ___ ___ ___
         21 26 17 17 9   21 19 6   21 23 19

___ ___ ___ ___ ___.
14 6   3   9   14

I begin near Torrington in western Connecticut and travel almost 40 miles until I meet up with the Housatonic River in Derby. I am the only major river that actually begins in Connecticut.

Use the Code Box below to write the letters above the numbered spaces.

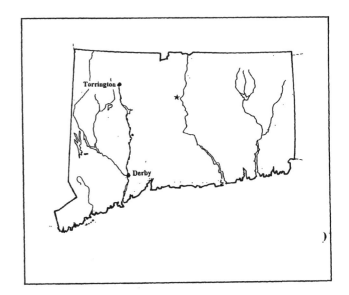

62

Code Box

S	J	V	D	X	I	Y	P	E	W	K	B	H
1	2	3	4	5	6	7	8	9	10	11	12	13

R	A	Q	N	G	T	L	C	M	U	Z	F	O
14	15	16	17	18	19	20	21	22	23	24	25	26

I flow south through the following towns before meeting the Housatonic River.

___ ___ ___ ___ ___ ___ ___ ___ ___   ___ ___ ___ ___ ___ ___ ___ ___ ___
10 15 19   9 14 12 23 14   7   13 15 14 10   6 17 19 26 17

___ ___ ___   ___ ___ ___ ___ ___ ___ ___ ___ ___.
15 17   4   19 13 26 22 15   1 19 26 17

I am the ___ ___ ___ ___ ___ ___ ___ ___ ___   ___ ___ ___ ___ ___.
         17 15 23 18 15 19 23 21 11   14   6   3   9 14

Connecticut Rivers Word Search

The Connecticut River runs through the middle of the state but there are several other rivers throughout the area. Find and circle the rivers listed below. Names are listed horizontally, vertically and diagonally.

COGINCHAUG
FARMINGTON
FIVEMILE
HOCKANUM
HOUSATONIC
MOUNT HOPE
NATCHAUG
NAUGATUCK
POMPERAUG
POQUONOCK
QUINNIPIAC
SALMON
SHEPAUG
STILL
WEEKEEPEEMEE
YANTIC

H	S	E	G	U	A	R	E	P	M	O	P	Y	Y
O	W	A	E	L	I	M	E	V	I	F	A	P	U
U	D	E	L	P	T	W	E	T	E	N	G	O	A
S	G	G	E	M	Q	K	M	Y	T	U	G	Q	C
A	E	U	V	K	O	C	R	I	A	C	U	U	A
T	K	A	Y	E	E	N	C	H	O	M	A	O	I
O	C	H	F	I	O	E	C	V	S	I	P	N	P
N	U	C	E	Z	S	N	P	S	D	R	E	O	I
I	T	T	C	V	I	N	C	E	T	L	H	C	N
C	A	A	R	G	P	C	U	U	E	I	S	K	N
U	G	N	O	O	C	B	W	Q	Q	M	L	V	I
Q	U	C	H	O	C	K	A	N	U	M	E	L	U
L	A	C	E	P	O	H	T	N	U	O	M	E	Q
I	N	A	M	N	O	T	G	N	I	M	R	A	F

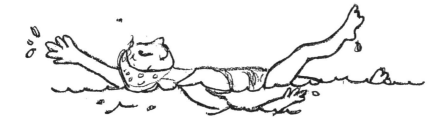

Nathan Hale Cross-Outs

Can you imagine that even though Nathan Hale was only 21 years old when he was executed, we still remember him today for his courage and patriotism? He fought bravely in the Revolutionary War for our independence. During the war, George Washington himself asked for a volunteer to spy on the English troops in New York. Nathan Hale bravely agreed and entered New York pretending to be a school master. But he was soon caught with notes about the troops hidden in his shoes and was sentenced to die. Just before his death he wrote a farewell letter to his mother and one to a fellow officer. But the English cruelly destroyed his letters and hanged the young hero from an apple tree.

He was executed in New York City near what is now 66th and Third Avenue. His last words were, "I only regret that I have but one life to lose for my country."

Follow the instructions below to find two interesting facts about Nathan Hale.

1. Cross out 4 boys names.
2. Cross out 3 kinds of birds.
3. Cross out 4 flowers.
4. Cross out 3 colors.

BOB	HE	PETUNIA	ROBIN	WAS
BORN	JACK	EAGLE	IN	ROSE
WILLIAM	COVENTRY	HAWK	DAISY	CONNECTICUT
YELLOW	SAM	PANSY	RED	ORANGE

1. Cross out 3 states.
2. Cross out 3 trees.
3. Cross out 3 school supplies.

MICHIGAN	HE	MAPLE	WAS	MAINE
ONE	PINE	OF	OHIO	PENS
PENCILS	TWELVE	OAK	CHILDREN	NOTEBOOK

Famous Nutmeg Philanthropists

"What the heck is a philanthropist" you might be saying. Well, first the word is pronounced like this: fil- an' throp-ist

A philanthropist is someone who gives money to charitable causes that make peoples lives better and help the world. When children have a lemonade stand and give their earnings to their school or hurricane victims, they are young philanthropists.

Daniel Wadsworth, Philanthropist (1771-1848)

Wadsworth was born the son of a wealthy slave owner. But he grew up with a strong commitment to making the world a better place. He gave food to people in need and helped to build the state's first hospital for the mentally ill. He also helped to create the Hartford Orphan Asylum.

But he is perhaps best known for establishing the first public art museum in America. The Wadsworth Atheneum is still located on Main Street in Hartford.

Paul Newman, Actor and Philanthropist (1925-   )

For many years Paul Newman was known as the famous movie actor with the striking blue eyes. One day he and his friend decided to bottle their own recipe for Italian salad dressing and donate the profits to charity. People loved his recipe and he started to sell other kinds of salad dressing as well as popcorn. He has made millions of dollars from the sales of Newman's Own food items and donated all the profits to various charities that have helped thousands of people. He lives in Connecticut with his wife, the actress Joanne Woodward.

You're A Philanthropist

If you become a philanthropist, what causes would you give your money and your time to help make the world a better place? You have a million dollars to give away. Tell us what you would do with it.

_____, Philanthropist
Print your name here

I would want to donate money to _____
_____
_____
_____
_____
_____
_____
_____
_____
_____

Besides giving money, how might you volunteer your time somewhere to make the world a better place?

_____
_____
_____
_____
_____
_____
_____
_____

Famous Nutmeg Storytellers

Sam Clemens, Storyteller (1835-1910)

While he was born Sam Clemens in Florida in 1835, this author is better known by his pen name, Mark Twain. In 1874, he moved his family to Hartford, Connecticut and built a lovely house on a hill. His next door neighbor was the famous author, Harriet Beecher Stowe.

Mark Twain was known for his great sense of humor. Some of his books that you may want to read are *The Adventures of Huckleberry Finn, A Connecticut Yankee in King Arthur's Court,* and *Tom Sawyer.*

Maurice Sendak, Children's book author and illustrator (1928 -)

Maurice Sendak's wildly imaginative books include *Where the Wild Things Are, Outside Over There* and *In the Night Kitchen.* His parents were poor Polish immigrants. He didn't care much for school and wasn't very good at sports but he loved to read and draw. In addition to his children's books, he has designed sets and costumes for operas. He lives and works in Ridgefield, Connecticut.

You have been asked to write a story for young children. In the space below, tell us about that story.

Title:_____

_____

_____

_____

_____

_____

_____

_____

_____

_____

_____

_____

_____

Famous Nutmegger's Crossword Puzzle

After you have read about the two philanthropists and two authors on the previous pages, see if you can do this crossword.

ACROSS
1. Twain had a great sense of _____
3. Newman makes salad dressings and _____
5. Twain's novel titled *Tom* _____.
9. Sam Clemens' pen name (two words)
10. Philanthropists give _____ to charity
12. Paul Newman's first career
13. Sam Clemens was born in this state
14. Mark Twain's novel, *The Adventures of Huckleberry* _____
15. Clemens lived next door to Harriet Beecher _____

DOWN
1. City where Clemens built his home
2. Wadsworth helped establish the first public art _____
4. Wadsworth helped create the Hartford _____ Asylum
6. Clemens' book *A Connecticut* _____ *in King Arthur's Court*
7. Newman's first type of salad dressing
8. Sendak's parents were poor Polish _____
11. Sendak designs sets and costumes for _____

Famous Nutmeggers and You

Of the four famous Nutmeggers we've read about, which one do you most admire?

_____

Why?_____

_____

_____

_____

If you could ask this person a question, what would you ask?

_____

_____

_____

_____

_____

_____

Another Famous Nutmegger

To learn about another famous Connecticut individual answer the nine clues below. Then write each letter in the matching numbered box at the bottom of the page to spell out the fact.

1. Boxing match winner

$\overline{25}\ \overline{6}\ \overline{9}\ \overline{10}\ \overline{23}$

2. Strolled

$\overline{14}\ \overline{17}\ \overline{12}\ \overline{38}\ \overline{31}\ \overline{1}$

3. Physically powerful

$\overline{37}\ \overline{5}\ \overline{3}\ \overline{27}\ \overline{18}\ \overline{26}$

4. Every 24 hours

$\overline{32}\ \overline{33}\ \overline{24}\ \overline{13}\ \overline{7}$

5. Mid-day

$\overline{16}\ \overline{2}\ \overline{4}\ \overline{36}$

6. Person, place or _____

$\overline{40}\ \overline{8}\ \overline{35}\ \overline{42}\ \overline{43}$

70

7. Greasy

$\overline{19}\ \overline{41}\ \overline{28}\ \overline{21}$

8. A woman gangster

$\overline{22}\ \overline{15}\ \overline{20}\ \overline{34}$

9. Female servant

$\overline{30}\ \overline{39}\ \overline{11}\ \overline{29}$

$\overline{}\ \overline{}\ \overline{}\ \overline{}\ \overline{}\ \overline{}\ \overline{}\quad \overline{}\ \overline{}\ \overline{}\ \overline{}\ \overline{}\ \overline{}\quad \overline{}\ \overline{}\ \overline{}$

1 2 3 4 5 6 7   8 9 10 11 12 13   14 15 16

$\overline{}\ \overline{}\quad \overline{}\ \overline{}\ \overline{}\ \overline{}\ \overline{}\ \overline{}\ \overline{}\quad \overline{}\ \overline{}\ \overline{}\ \overline{}$

17 18   19 20 21 22 23 24 25   26 27 28 29

$\overline{}\ \overline{}\ \overline{}\ \overline{}\ \overline{}\quad \overline{}\ \overline{}\quad \overline{}\ \overline{}\ \overline{}\ \overline{}\ \overline{}\ \overline{}\ \overline{}.$

30 31 32 33 34   35 36   37 38 39 40 41 42 43

Your Connecticut Alphabet

Authors and illustrators are always making new alphabet books about places and things that interest them. If you were to write and illustrate your own personal Alphabet of Connecticut, you might start with "A is for American Dream Museum" or "D is for Dinosaur State Park". In the following boxes design and then draw a picture for your own personal Connecticut Alphabet.

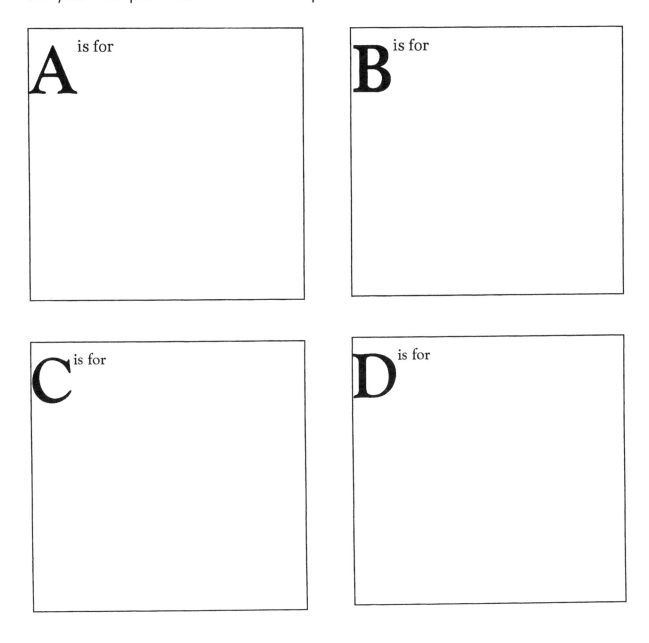

A is for

B is for

C is for

D is for

Your Connecticut Alphabet

E is for

F is for

72

G is for

H is for

Your Connecticut Alphabet

I is for

J is for

K is for

L is for

Your Connecticut Alphabet

M is for

N is for

74

O is for

P is for

Your Connecticut Alphabet

Q is for

R is for

S is for

T is for

Your Connecticut Alphabet

U is for

V is for

W is for

X is for

Your Connecticut Alphabet

Y is for

Z is for

Here are some suggestions:

A: American Dream Museum, *Amistad,* amusement park
B: Black Dog, Boomboy Parade, Bartlett Arboretum, bluefish, Beardsley Zoo
C: Charter Oak, covered bridges, Connecticut River, cotton gin, carousel
D: Dinosaur State Park, Discovery Museum
E: Essex Steam Train, East River Beach
F: Fairchild Wildflower Garden, ferry, fishing boats, farms
G: Gillette Castle, gardens, greenhouses
H: hiking, Housatonic River, Haddam Island
I: ice hockey, Indian Chair, islands
J: jazz festivals, Johnnycakes
K: Kent Falls, Kidcity Children's Museum
L: Litchfield Hills, lighthouse, lobster
M: Mystic Village, *Moby Dick*

N: nutmeg, New England Carousel Museum
O: oyster, Old Saybrook, Torchlight Parade, orchards
P: praying mantis, Puppet Museum, Pequot Indians, Pinchot Sycamore
Q: Quassy Amusement Park, Quaddick Mountain
R: robin, Riga Lake
S: Shore Line Trolley, submarine, shipwreck, sloop, schooners
T: Thimble Islands, trolleys, tourists
U: U.S.Coast Guard Academy
V: village greens, visitors
W: whaling ship, waterfalls, Woodstock Fair
X: x-country skiing, xmas trees
Y: Yankees, Yantic Falls, Yale University
Z: zoo, Zwick Point

Connecticut's Cities Word Search

Connecticut is known for its many charming towns but it is also famous for its bustling cities. Thousands of people live and work in these large communities. Find and circle the Connecticut cities listed below.

The names appear horizontally, vertically and diagonally.

T	O	R	R	I	N	G	T	O	N	T	O	D	H	V	G
C	T	M	V	M	I	R	M	I	C	A	Z	W	X	V	T
X	W	V	H	H	L	L	E	F	D	U	M	G	V	V	G
M	O	S	C	V	T	G	P	T	B	Y	C	A	A	T	I
V	K	G	M	C	C	D	R	R	S	Z	Z	F	Q	R	E
H	J	C	T	O	L	I	I	N	Y	E	G	R	E	K	P
C	P	X	U	Z	J	D	E	L	K	R	H	O	Y	I	H
I	N	J	B	S	G	W	C	G	K	L	U	C	D	F	E
W	Y	H	E	E	L	N	W	V	K	A	A	B	N	P	D
R	W	A	P	O	E	F	N	T	K	F	L	W	N	A	X
O	K	O	N	D	W	V	L	V	M	J	O	K	R	A	M
N	R	D	I	E	F	W	T	D	R	L	Y	P	Y	O	D
T	O	R	S	T	R	A	D	R	O	F	M	A	T	S	N
N	E	M	X	G	C	R	Q	N	E	V	A	H	W	E	N
M	H	A	R	T	F	O	R	D	A	T	D	W	U	P	X
V	L	K	L	M	F	H	Y	R	U	B	R	E	T	A	W

BRIDGEPORT
DANBURY
HARTFORD
MANCHESTER
MERIDEN
NEW HAVEN

NEW LONDON
NORWALK
NORWICH
STAMFORD
TORRINGTON
WATERBURY

Connecticut Firsts

It's truly incredible how many items were first produced in our state. Everything from the first artificial heart to the first lollipop! Below is a list of several items that were first built or produced in the great state of Connecticut. See how many you can find and circle.

```
P I V A C U U M C L E A N E R N P A C
O C C H E L I C O P T E R Y F O F A Z
L T O E T M Z J I Q M G Y Y P A N W Q
A O R L M Y I H P Q K N M I R O G N E
R W H O O A L U B A A D L T P M E R N
O N L L Q R K Y R J C L I E F V M Y I
I L T G Y D T E U K O F N R M J B R H
D I L L M H E E R L I E E F V O D A C
C B H S O Z Q Z L C R D A C C H V N A
A R W P Z A Z F I E C P P D V G I O M
M A N E L Z R A H L V O A L V F W I G
E R A Z H I L A P G R I T Y Z M U T N
R Y Q Y S H M L O S C L S T P E X C I
A M Z B E B F M H N P H C I O H D I W
L B E A U T T L P K R G D C O N O D E
O E R R S T A T E H O U S E J N G N S
V T G N E N O I T U T I T S N O C I E
E E C S P Y R A R B I L C I L B U P N
R P U B L I C A R T M U S E U M X Q X
```

ARTIFICIAL HEART
CAN OPENER
COLOR TELEVISION
CONSTITUTION
COTTON GIN
DICTIONARY

FRISBEE
HAMBURGER
HELICOPTER
ICE MAKER
LOLLIPOP
PAY PHONE

POLAROID CAMERA
PUBLIC ART MUSEUM
PUBLIC LIBRARY
SEWING MACHINE
STATE HOUSE
TOWN LIBRARY
VACUUM CLEANER

America's First Cookbook

Early colonists had to adapt local foods to their English cookbooks until 1796 when Amelia Simmons wrote *American Cookery*. It was the first cookbook published in America by an American featuring American recipes and ingredients. It was an immediate bestseller. It featured colonial favorites like pumpkin pudding, winter squash pudding, roast mutton, gingerbread, and spruce beer. There was a recipe for Indian slapjacks, also known as Johnny Cakes.

Little is known about Amelia Simmons outside of what she reveals about herself in the book's preface. There she refers to herself as an "American Orphan" and goes on to say how female orphans are often reduced to working as maids or cooks. She is referred to in other writings as uneducated and even illiterate and indeed her cookbook has a co-author. Perhaps Amelia gathered the recipes and her co-author helped to write them.

80

How many of the 10 foods available during Colonial days can you unscramble?

1. morcalen _____

2. lsta _____

3. kmil _____

4. dnpudig _____

5. Otnumt _____

6. kseca _____

7. retbut _____

8. mrace _____

9. hqssau _____

10. ikpnump _____

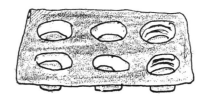

New England Johnny Cake Recipe

Long before Amelia Simmons gathered together her recipes, the Native Americans taught the colonists how to cook using maize (corn). They probably passed on the recipe for Johnny Cake as many recipes remain from that period. It was also called journey cake as it could be easily stuffed into a traveler's pocket. During colonial times, Johnny Cakes were often served at every meal. Serve the cakes hot with butter and maple syrup.

1 cup yellow cornmeal
$\frac{1}{2}$ teaspoon salt
1 cup boiling water
$\frac{1}{2}$ cup milk

Mix the first two ingredients. Add the boiling water, stirring until smooth. Add the milk and stir well. Grease a heavy, 12-inch frying pan. Set over a medium low heat. Drop teaspoons of batter onto the pan and cook until golden brown, about five minutes. Turn the cakes and cook the other side for about five minutes. Makes about 12 cakes.

Where Are The Mountains?

Connecticut's highest mountains are in the northwestern section of the state. Mount Frissell is the highest point in the state. Bear Mountain, Mount Gridley, Mount Riga and Bradford Mountain are also located in this area.

Question: What is the name of the section of the state where these mountains are located?

Fill in the missing letter in the names of Connecticut cities and towns listed below. When all the letters are written in, read down the column for the answer.

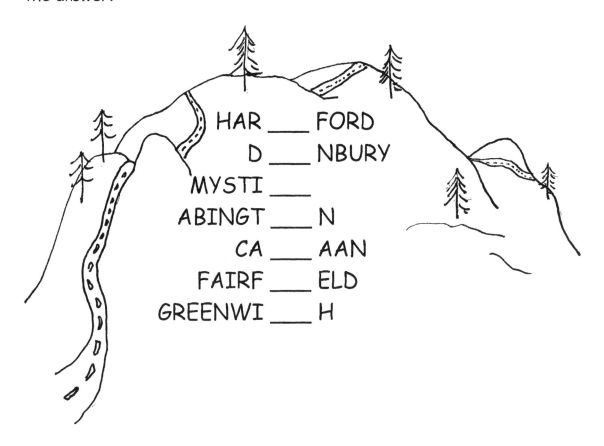

HAR ___ FORD

D ___ NBURY

MYSTI ___

ABINGT ___ N

CA ___ AAN

FAIRF ___ ELD

GREENWI ___ H

Answer: It is the _____ Section.

Names and Addresses

Here are the names and addresses/web sites of some places in Connecticut that I want to investigate. If I can't get to them in person, I can check them out on the web.

Write About You in Connecticut

Write about something interesting that has happened to you in Connecticut. It can be one sentence or the whole page.

_____

_____

_____

_____

_____

_____

_____

_____

_____

_____

_____

The end 4 now! ☺

PAGE 7 Lighthouse Logic

PAGE 9 Hiking Litchfield Hills

#__7__ #__9__ #__25__ #__12__ #__15__

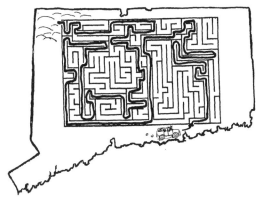

PAGE 8   Connecticut Counties
Word Search

PAGE 10   Noah Webster

85

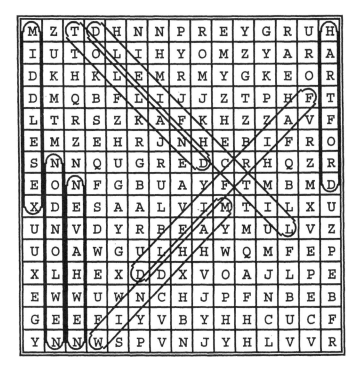

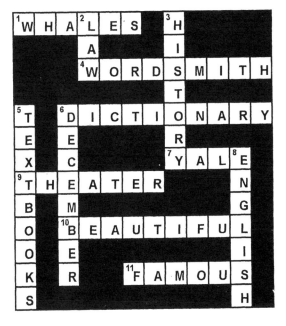

PAGE 11   Sea Glass

PAGE 13   Beardsley Zoo
Word Search

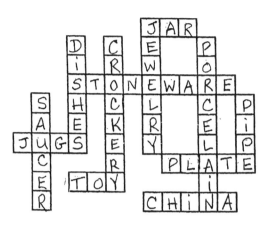

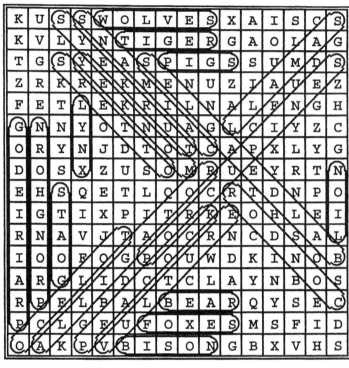

86

PAGE 12 What's Our Largest City?

BEAR
RACOON
LION
CONDOR
ALLIGATOR
FOXES
PIGS
BISON
OTTERS
TIGERS

Answer: Bridgeport

PAGE 14   Missing Letters

M	S	M
Y	E	U
S	A	S
T	P	E
I	O	U
C	R	M
	T	

PAGE 15   Good Neighbors

PAGE 18   How Many Miles?

1.   4 miles
2. 58 miles
3. 28 miles
4. 51 miles
5. 48 miles
6. 57 miles

Answer: 246 miles

87

PAGE 16   Secret Messages

1. The Connecticut River
2. Rev. Thomas Hooker
3. The American Robin
4. New Haven

PAGE 17   Connecticut Museums

1. Essex
2. Bridgeport
3. Manchester
4. Bristol

PAGE 20   Lake Candlewood
Word Search

PAGE 21   Mitten Match

PAGE 23   Word Pyramids
(Here are some possibilities.)

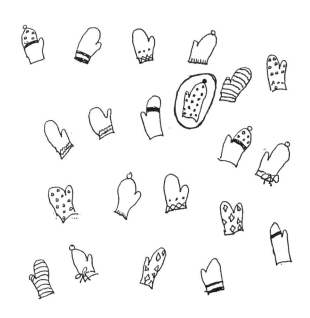

88

PAGE 22 More Connecticut
     Museums

1. EAST WINDSOR
2. MYSTIC
3. NORWALK
4. MIDDLETOWN

PAGE 24 "The Nutmeg State"
     Cross-Outs

1. THE SPICE COMES FROM THE
TREE'S BROWN SEEDS.

2. NUTMEG IS A SWEET SPICY
FLAVOR.

PAGE 26   Nutmeg in a Maze

PAGE 35   The Leatherman Maze

PAGE 27   Still More Connecticut
Museums

1. NIANTIC
2. NEW HAVEN
3. BRISTOL
4. WEST HARTFORD

PAGE 28 Connecticut Favorites

CHILD	Oysters	Robins	Clams	Lobsters
Bill	X	X	X	O
Sarah	O	X	X	X
Bob	X	X	O	X
Sue	X	O	X	X

PAGE 36   Pirate's Maze

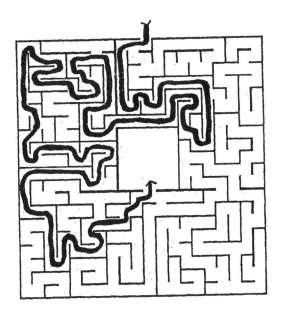

PAGE 37   Connecticut Legends
          Crossword Puzzle

PAGE 38   CT

1. CAT
2. CENT
3. COAST
4. CARROT
5. CONSENT
6. CHESTNUT

PAGE 39   Long Island Sound

1. THE CONNECTICUT, HOUSATONIC, AND THAMES RIVERS.

2. NORWALK and the Marinelife Aquarium in ESSEX.

PAGE 40   Mapping Connecticut

(Remember, these numbers are approximate. Yours may be slightly different.)
1. 48 miles
2. 48 miles
3. 19 miles
4. 62 miles
5. 79 miles
6. 43 miles
7. 10 miles
8. 60 miles
9. 35 miles

ALL THE ANSWERS

PAGE 42   Beaches Criss Cross

PAGE 44   Tide Pooling Criss Cross

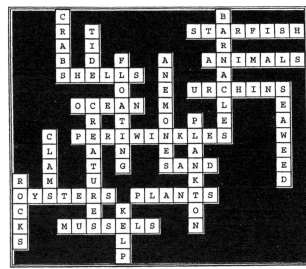

PAGE 43   Counting Seashells

A. Tim = 20 shells
B. John = 12 shells
C. Katie = 8 shells
D. Melanie = 7 shells
E. Will = 5 shells
Melanie's collection = 7 shells

PAGE 46   Categories
(Here are some possibilities.)

	T	H	I	R	D
Animal or bird	tiger, thrush, tadpole, turkey	hog, hen, hummingbird, horse, hare, hedgehog	ibis, ibex, iguana, impala	rodent, rat, rabbit, racoon, reindeer	dog, deer, duck, dove, dingo, donkey
Words containing the letter "A"	toad, today, trace, tribal	had, handle, hoard	Indian, air, Indiana, irate,	raid, radar, read, relay, reveal,	dare, darling, danger, daffodil
Things found outdoors	turkey, trees, tractor	hills, highways,	island, ivy, inchworm, icebergs, icicles	river, road, rattlesnake, rodeo, ranch, railroad	driveway, deck, dirt, doorknob, docks,
Things found in the kitchen	toaster, tea, toaster, thyme	hot dogs, horseradish,	ice, ice cream,	raddish, refrigerator, rags, relish,	dishes, drinks, disposal, dishwasher
Girl's names	Teresa, Tina, Taylor, Tiffany	Holly, Hannah, Heather, Hillary	Iris, Ingrid, Irene	Rachel, Rene, Rose, Rita, Rhonda,	Debby, Donna, Diane, Dede, Dolly
Boy's names	Tom, Ted, Taylor, Tim, Tyler	Henry, Harry, Harvey, Herman	Irving, Iain, Ivan	Robert, Ray, Ronan, Riley, Randy, Ron	Daniel, Dick, David,

91

PAGE 47 Climbing Mount Frissell

Clues
1. Paid money for something
   bought
2. The state capital of Connecticut
   Hartford
3. Worn when it gets chilly
   sweater
4. Needed to mail a letter
   stamp
5. Find it in a garden flower
6. A car engine motor
7. Connecticut's hottest month
   July
8. Window decoration curtain
9. You read it book
10. Four weeks or 30 days
    month
11. Great affection love

2,380 feet

red · love
thing · month
tree · curtain · book
July · motor · autumn
gorilla · flower · stamp
rain · bologna · sweater
Hartford · Trumbull · Sharon
bought · fought · thought

92

PAGE 48 How's the Weather?

1. SNOWSTORM
2. HAIL
3. HUMIDITY
4. BLIZZARD
5. HURRICANE
6. LIGHTNING
7. FOG
8. THUNDER
9. SUNSHINE
10. WIND
11. SLEET
12. RAIN

PAGE 51 The Amistad Case

Answer: Farmington

PAGE 52 Amistad Maze

PAGE 53 An Oyster Eating Contest

A. Taylor ate 16
B. Emily ate 12
C. Sam ate 10
D. Gabe ate 6
E. Holly ate 4

PAGE 55   Connecticut Fairs and Festivals

1. NEW HAVEN
2. ESSEX
3. MYSTIC SEAPORT
4. BRIDGEPORT

PAGE 56 Connecticut's Oldest Fair

The Four Town Fair got its name because it began by traveling through each of the four towns until it found its permanent home at the EGYPT ROAD fairgrounds in SOMERS. The Fair takes place in SEPTEMBER each year.   There is a FROG JUMPING and largest FROG contest. Come to the Four Town Fair to see the DOODLEBUG, RACING PIGS and the area's largest PUMPKIN.

PAGE 57 Connecticut Puzzle Tournament

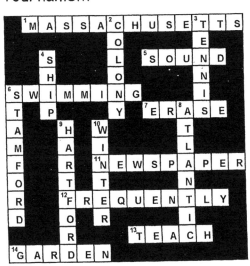

PAGE 58   Pequot Cross-Outs

THEY BELIEVED THAT LAND BELONGED TO NO ONE.

THEY RAISED CORN, BEANS, SQUASH AND TOBACCO.

PAGE 60   Thimble Island Criss- Cross

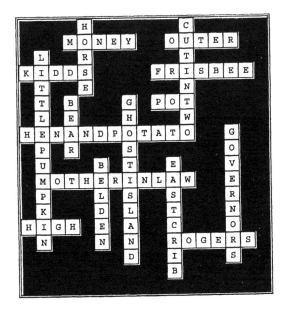

PAGE 61 What River Am I? # 1

I am New England's longest river. I am the Connecticut River

PAGE 62   What River Am I? #2

Waterbury, Harwinton and Thomaston. I am the Naugatuck River.

PAGE 63 Connecticut Rivers Word Search

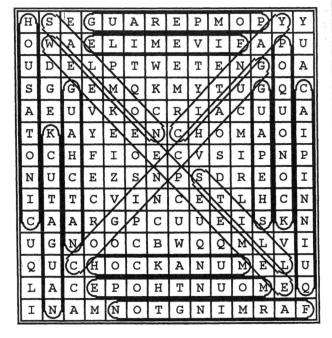

94

PAGE 64   Nathan Hale Cross-Outs

HE WAS BORN IN COVENTRY, CONNECTICUT.

HE WAS ONE OF TWELVE CHILDREN.

PAGE 68 Famous Nutmegger's Crossword Puzzle

PAGE 70 Another Famous Nutmegger

1. CHAMP
2. WALKED
3. STRONG
4. DAILY
5. NOON
6. THING
7. OILY
8. MOLL
9. MAID

DOROTHY HAMILL WON AN OLYMPIC GOLD MEDAL IN SKATING.

PAGE 78   Connecticut Cities Word Search

```
T O R R I N G T O N T O D H V G
C T M V M I R M I C A Z W X V T
X W V H H L L E F D U M G V V G
M O S C V T G P T B Y C A A T I
V K G M C C D R R S Z Z F Q R E
H J C T O L I I N Y E G R E K P
C P X U Z J D E L R R H O Y I H
I N J B S G W C G K L U C D F E
W Y H E E L N W V K A A B N P D
R W A P O E F N T K F L W N A X
O K O N D W V L V M J O K R A M
N R D I E F W T D R L Y P Y O D
T O R S T R A D R O F M A T S N
N E M X G C R Q N E V A H W E N
M H A R T F O R D A T D W U P X
V L K L M F H Y R U B R E T A W
```

PAGE 80   America's First Cookbook

1. cornmeal
2. salt
3. milk
4. pudding
5. mutton
6. cakes
7. butter
8. cream
9. squash
10. pumpkin

PAGE 82   Where Are The Mountains?

Answer: It is the <u>TACONIC</u> Section.

PAGE 70   Connecticut Firsts

```
P I V A C U U M C L E A N E R N P A C
O C C H E L I C O P T E R Y F O A Z
L T O E T M Z J I Q M G Y Y B A N W Q
A O R L M Y I H P Q K N M I B O G N E
R W H O A L U B A A D L T P M E R N
O N L L Q R K Y R J C L I E F V M Y I
I L T G Y D T E U K O E N R M J B R H
D I L L M H E E R L I E E F V O D A C
C B H S O Z Q Z I C R D A C C H V N A
A R W P Z A Z B I E C P P D V G I O M
M A N E L Z R A H L V O A L V F W I G
E R A Z H I L A P G R I T Y Z M U T N
R Y Q Y S H M L O S C L S T P E X C I
A M Z B E B F M H N P H C I O H D I W
L B E A U T T L P K R G D C O N O D E
O E R R S T A T E H O U S E J N G N S
V T G N E N O I T U T I T S N O C I
F E C S P Y R A R B I L C I L B U P N
R P U B L I C A R T M U S E U M X Q X
```

95